This potty book
belongs to
....

A Note to Parents and Carers

Sharing this book with a child can be helpful in preparing them for toilet training.
Children will be fascinated to discover that everybody poos, even animals!
This can make going on the potty seem much more natural. At the end of the story are some confidence-boosting tips for you to read together, and here are some hints that might help you:

* Potty training can start as early as eighteen months, but most children may not be ready until three years of age or after.
* When learning any new skill, children need lots of patient guidance and encouragement.
* When you think your child might be ready, get a potty. Set aside a week or even longer for just potty training, and let everyone know. Don't expect to get anything else done that week!
* Let your toddler get used to the potty with no pressure.
* Encourage lots of potty practice! If a child has an accident don't make an issue out of it.
* Aim to phase out nappies in the daytime first, and once this is working, with a little encouragement, nights will become dry too.
* A goal for the child can be a good incentive. "If you are dry all day, we will do this . . ."
* If it works celebrate, celebrate, CELEBRATE!

For Harriet the super-pooper
Love, Daddy

ZOO POO
A RED FOX BOOK 0 09 945652 4
First published in Great Britain by Red Fox,
an imprint of Random House Children's Books
This edition published 2004
1 3 5 7 9 10 8 6 4 2

Red Fox Books are published by Random House Children's Books, 61–63 Uxbridge Road, London W5 5SA,
a division of The Random House Group Ltd London, Sydney, Johannesburg, Auckland and agencies throughout the world
THE RANDOM HOUSE GROUP Limited Reg. No. 954009
A CIP catalogue record for this book is available from the British Library.
Printed in Hong Kong
www.kidsatrandomhouse.co.uk

Richard Morgan

RED FOX

"How do you doo-doo at the zoo?"

Kangaroos doo-doo while on the hop.

Elephants doo-doo bigger than you. Plop!

Giraffes
doo-doo from
way up high.

Rhinos doo-doo as they charge on by.

Toucans doo-doo
as they fly in the sky.

Zebras doo-doo while having a munch.

Tigers doo-doo to make room for lunch.

Watch Out!

And cheeky monkeys doo-doo
right in front of you!

"But I'm not like
any of you . . .
I poo in the loo!"

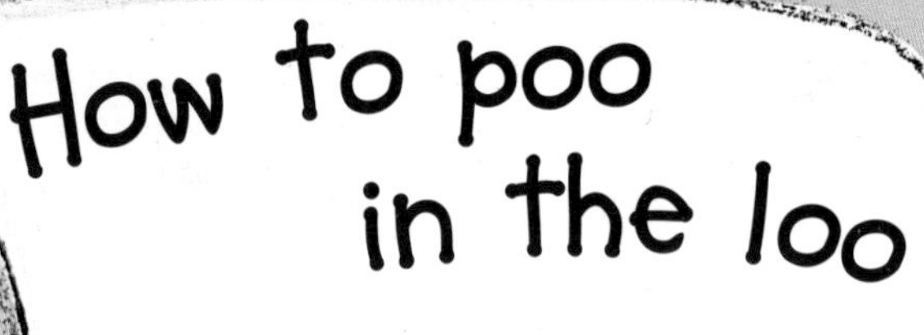

I like to sit on the loo after breakfast, lunch and supper, before my bath and even just for fun. We always clap and say I'm clever.

If I doo-doo anything in the loo, I get even more claps and smiles.

"I'm sooo clever!"

We always wash our hands and dry them when we finish.

Now I use the loo all the time.

Charlie x